The Graphic Novel

BEAUTY and the BEAST

RETOLD BY MICHAEL DAHL
ILLUSTRATED

www.raintreepublishers.co.uk
Visit our website to find out
more information about
Raintree books.

To order:
☎ Phone 0845 6044371
🖨 Fax +44 (0) 1865 312263
📧 Email myorders@raintreepublishers.co.uk

Customers from outside the UK please telephone +44 1865 312262

Raintree is an imprint of Capstone Global Library Limited, a company incorporated in
England and Wales having its registered office at 7 Pilgrim Street, London EC4V 6LB
Registered company number: 6695882

Text © Stone Arch Books 2009
First published by Stone Arch Books in 2009
First published in paperback in the United Kingdom by Capstone Global Library in 2013
The moral rights of the proprietor have been asserted.

Editor: Laura Knowles
Art Director: Heather Kindseth
Graphic Designer: Kay Fraser
Librarian Reviewer: Katharine Kan
Reading Consultant: Elizabeth Stedem
Printed and bound in China by CTPS

ISBN 978 1 406 24317 8 (paperback)
16 15 14 13 12
10 9 8 7 6 5 4 3 2 1

British Library Cataloguing in Publication Data
Dahl, Michael.
Beauty and the beast. -- (Graphic spin)
741.5-dc23
A full catalogue record for this book is available from the British Library.

CAST OF CHARACTERS

THE SISTERS

THE FATHER

BEAUTY

THE BEAST

Many years ago, in a faraway kingdom, in a town that sat by the sea . . .

A rich merchant lived at the top of a high hill with his three daughters.

The youngest daughter was the loveliest and the kindest of the three. So the merchant called her Beauty.

9

All my poor roses have been ruined by summer storms.

Father, if you wish to bring me something, bring me a rose.

Just one rose? Is that all?

Then it will be the most perfect rose I can find, my dear.

It will be enough.

You have stolen one of my roses!

Please, sir. I only meant it as a gift for my daughter, Beauty.

Here take it back!

I should eat you here and now. Instead, I shall give you another chance.

Send your daughter, Beauty. I want to see what this creature looks like who demands something that is not her own.
Now go! Go before I change my mind and give in to my hunger!

Because Beauty loved her father, she agreed to visit the monster the very next morning.

This is the place that Father described.

Beauty told the creature that she wanted them to be good friends.

But at the end of every dinner, it was always the same.

Beauty, will you marry me?

I'm sorry, but I cannot marry you.

How could I marry a beast?

23

Please, Beauty. Do not leave me alone in this dark castle.

I promise that I will return in one week.

The Beast did not tell Beauty that there was a special magic to his castle. It was a place ruled by promises.

If Beauty broke her promise, and did not return to the castle in a week's time, then the Beast would die.

At the merchant's house . . .

. . . it was a happy reunion.

That night, Beauty told the family about her time with the beast.

Beauty, now that you have escaped the Beast, you must never go back.

But I gave him my word that I would return.

He's a monster! Promises mean nothing to a creature like that!

Besides, we are your family. You must stay with us.

In truth, Beauty's sisters were a little jealous. They saw the fine clothes and precious jewels that the Beast had given her as presents.

Beauty was confused. She had given the Beast her word she would return. But her family would be heartbroken if she left them again.

I am happy to be home, but something is wrong. I don't feel the same.

Could I actually be missing the poor Beast?

One night, Beauty slipped out of her room. She had made up her mind to keep her promise.

But when she finally reached the castle . . .

You said you would come back in a week. You promised.

Please forgive me. My family wanted me to stay.

It is too late now anyway. I am dying.

No! No! You cannot die, dear Beast. I love you!

And they lived happily together, forever.

ABOUT THE AUTHOR

Michael Dahl is the author of more than 100 books for children and young adults. He has won awards for his non-fiction, and his Finnegan Zwake mystery series was chosen by the Agatha Awards to be among the five best mystery books for children in 2002 and 2003. He collects books on poison and graveyards, and lives in a haunted house.

ABOUT THE ILLUSTRATOR

Luke Feldman is an illustrator, animator, and designer from Australia. For more than 10 years, he has worked on high-profile projects for large corporations such as Microsoft and Coca Cola. He has also worked closely with the Australian education department, developing animations and interactive games for children.

GLOSSARY

carriage vehicle with wheels, often pulled by horses

courageous brave or fearless

demand ask for something firmly

describe create a picture of something in words

expensive costing a lot of money

kindness if someone shows kindness, he or she is being friendly, helpful, and generous

loyal firm in supporting or faithful to one's country, family, friends, or beliefs

maiden young, unmarried woman

merchant someone who sells goods for profit

precious rare and valuable

reunion meeting between people who have not seen each other for a long time

tenderness if someone shows tenderness, he or she is being gentle or kind

THE HISTORY OF BEAUTY AND THE BEAST

The tale of BEAUTY AND THE BEAST begins hundreds of years ago. Even before it was first written down, the story was passed from person to person for many generations.

Partly inspired by these oral tales, French author Madame Gabrielle de Villeneuve wrote the earliest known version of BEAUTY AND THE BEAST in 1740. Villeneuve meant for her story to be read by adults rather than children. The novella, or medium-length story, was nearly as long as a novel. It contained many parts that were later taken out, including information about the beast's childhood. Possibly the biggest difference, however, comes at the end of Villeneuve's tale. In her version, the beast is never transformed back into a prince. This part of the story was added 16 years later.

In 1756, another French author named Madame Le Prince de Beaumont crafted the best-known version of the fairy tale. Beaumont's tale was much shorter than Villeneuve's story. It was also aimed at younger readers. The new version quickly became popular, and a year later the story had been translated from French to English.

Since then, the story has been retold thousands of times in books, plays, and on film. On 13 November 1991, the Walt Disney Company released the animated version of BEAUTY AND THE BEAST in cinemas. The film quickly became a success. It is the only animated film to ever be nominated for an Academy Award (Oscar) for Best Picture.

DISCUSSION QUESTIONS

1. Beauty's father asks his daughters what they would like him to bring back from his trip. Two of the daughters want dresses and jewels, but Beauty wants just one rose. What does this tell you about Beauty's character? What kind of person is she?

2. Beauty's family didn't want her to return to the Beast's castle. Why do you think Beauty chose to return anyway?

3. Fairy tales are often told over and over again. Have you heard the Beauty and the Beast fairy tale before? How is this version of the story different from other versions you've heard, seen, or read?

WRITING PROMPTS

1. Fairy tales are fantasy stories, often about wizards, goblins, giants, and fairies. Many fairy tales have a happy ending. Write your own fairy tale. Then, read it to a friend or family member.

2. Beauty's father said that his daughters could have anything they wished for. If you could have anything, what would it be? Describe why you made that choice.

3. The story says that Beauty and the Beast "live happily together, forever". Write a story about their life together. Will they get married? Will Beauty's family come to live with them? Use your imagination.

OTHER BOOKS IN THE SERIES

Jack and the Beanstalk	978 1 406 24319 2
Red Riding Hood	978 1 406 24772 5
Sleeping Beauty	978 1 406 24771 8

MORE FAIRY TALES TO ENJOY

The book may be over, but the adventure is just beginning. There are many other exciting and fantastical tales for you to discover:

Grimm's Fairy Tales (Usborne Illustrated), Ruth Brocklehurst (Usborne, 2010)

Hans Christian Andersen's Fairy Tales (Usborne Illustrated), (Usborne, 2011)